So what should you be zapping i...

Try It Now!

Wherever you see the interactive icon you'll be able to unlock a fun experience to enjoy on your device. There are nine scattered throughout the Annual and one on the front cover to discover. See if you can find them all.

ZAP NOW!

Ready

Open Zappar on your device.

Aim

Scan the code on the page.

Zap

Then point your device at the page and watch it come to life!

A few helpful tips...

To get the best possible experience here are a few hints and tips:

- Connect to wifi if you can and the experiences will download even quicker than on 3G.
- Try and keep the pages as flat as you can for the best effect. Rest the Annual on a table or on the floor.
- Try and keep the full page in view from your phone after scanning the code. Don't get too close or far away if you can help it.

- Try and keep the pages clean and free from tears, pen and other marks as this may affect the experience.
- It's best to view the pages in good lighting conditions if you can.

If you're still having problems then do contact us at support@zappar.com and we'll do our best to help you.

Angry Birds Stella

Pedigree®

Published 2014. Pedigree Books Limited, Beech Hill House, Walnut Gardens, Exeter, Devon EX4 4DH.
www.pedigreebooks.com – books@pedigreegroup.co.uk
The Pedigree trademark, email and website addresses, are the sole and exclusive properties of Pedigree Group Limited, used under licence in this publication.

ROVIO BOOKS

ZAP NOW!

Stella's the leader of her flock. She looks cute and cuddly, but don't be fooled – push her too far and you'll see the feathers fly!

Stella is very loyal to her friends and she's always looking out for them. She doesn't like bullies though, and she has a blazing hot temper that they'd do well to avoid.

Stella loves doing new things and so she always tries to cram as much fun into her days as she can!

Stella's so ambitious that she sometimes takes on too much, but she figures if you don't try something you'll never know if you like it!

Stella is fast as the wind and she's perfected the art of blowing bubbles that she uses to keep herself and her special friends safe.

LOVES:
Singing,
Exploring.

FAVOURITE MODES
OF TRANSPORT:
Skateboard,
Parkour (running
and jumping
across everyday
objects as if
you're in the
gym!)

FAB FACT:

STELLA IS
THE ITALIAN
WORD
FOR STAR!

STELLA'S THE STAR!

Use the grid to draw Stella, then add your own spectacular background!

Stella might be smelling flowers or relaxing on the beach!

PICTURE 1 8

SPOT THE DIFFERENCE!

These two pictures look the same at first glance but they actually contain 8 differences!

Can you find them all?

PICTURE 2

ZAP NOW!

11

STELLA'S FRUIT SUSHI!

SURPRISE STRAWBERRIES!

Slice the top off a strawberry then add two pretty pieces of kiwi fruit in its place. Delicious!

BITE-SIZED BANANA!

Slice a banana into rounds. Lay the rounds on a plate and add small pieces of kiwi fruit and berries to decorate. Yummy!

NICKNAME: BAD PRINCESS

Gale isn't a real princess – she just thinks she is! She's beautiful, clever and charismatic. She used to be best friends with Stella, but Gale became blinded by pride, vanity and power. Now she's obsessed with finding the mysterious and mythical Golden Egg, even though it means she's not friends with Stella anymore. Whether she'll actually ever find the Golden Egg, no one knows...

The Bad Princess loves being the centre of attention – after all, she pretends to be a princess! So she loves all the fuss and care she gets from her Minion Pigs. However, she secretly misses her old friends – especially Stella – and hopes they'll get back together one day.

FAB FACT:

HER SPECIAL CROWN HELPS HER TO COMMAND THE PIGS – WHILE SHE'S WEARING IT THEY ARE COMPELLED TO OBEY BECAUSE THEY THINK SHE'S A ROYAL!

LOVES:
Power,
Being bossy!

FAVOURITE MODES OF TRANSPORT:
Swan Boat,
Piggy Princess Carriage.

SCHEMES & DREAMS!

The Bad Princess is eager to get her hands on the Golden Egg. But locating it is proving very difficult. Take a look at some of the failed attempts that she dreamt up.

ATTEMPT 1...BLINGSHOT!

THE PLAN: **Survey the land from high above by launching a pig from a slingshot.**

WHAT ACTUALLY HAPPENED: **Pig got tangled in slingshot while the flock watched on.**

ATTEMPT 2...EGG POACH COACH!

THE PLAN: **Minion Pig orchestra sing so beautifully that the Egg appears and rolls to them.**

WHAT ACTUALLY HAPPENED: **Pigs forgot the words and the tune.**

ATTEMPT 3...THE LOW DOWN DOWN-LOW!

THE PLAN: **Burrow underground to locate the Golden Egg's mysterious hiding place.**

WHAT ACTUALLY HAPPENED: **Pig kept tunnelling until he ended up in the sea! Splash!**

ATTEMPT 4...

THE PLAN:

WHAT ACTUALLY HAPPENED:

OPPOSITES

Stella and the Bad Princess used to be best friends. But, as Gale became more and more obsessed with the Golden Egg, it was clear the two friends wanted different things and they grew further and further apart. Here's how these two feisty chicks compare...

STELLA

FRIENDS:	Willow, Poppy, Dahlia, Luca; plus some bad-tempered birds over on Piggy Island!
LIKES:	Action and adventure!
FAVOURITE COLOUR:	Pink!
BEST QUALITY:	Caring for her friends.
SPECIAL SKILLS:	Blowing bubbles of any shape and size.
WHAT MAKES HER ANGRY:	When someone underestimates her or stands in her way, or when someone tries to bully her or her pals.
LOVES:	Singing, dressing up.
MOTTO:	"Firm, fair and FUN!"

NICKNAME: DREAMER

Willow's a dreamer, a lover not a hater and she's the artist of the flock. She lives in her own "Willow World" and dreams big! Willow likes big hats-and she can be a bit shy so they're great to hide beneath!

It ruffles her feathers to see those pigs behaving badly and destroying their natural habitat while they search for the Golden Egg. However, she has a pretty cool trick that she plays on them – she creates artistic images that can fool those dumb pigs any day of the week!

Willow cares a lot about the environment and often talks with the smaller critters that live on Golden Island to get a sense of what's really happening there.

LOVES:
Dreaming,
Art.

FAVOURITE MODES
OF TRANSPORT:
Her imagination!

FAB FACT:

A WILLOW IS
A TYPE OF TREE THAT HAS
SOME HELPFUL MEDICAL
PROPERTIES – IT'S EVEN USED
TO MAKE ASPIRIN!

DREAM IT, DO IT!

Willow loves to dream. Can you draw what she's dreaming about this time, then add some colour to Willow and her dreams?

DREAM PARTY!

Willow's hosting her dream party. Can you help by writing what they could eat and what music they could listen to? Think about what you'd like to eat and what your favourite songs are.

MENU

MUSIC

MAKE WILLOW'S DREAM CATCHER

Dream Catchers were created by Native Americans to encourage and hold sweet dreams.

You can make your own by following these instructions.

YOU WILL NEED:

- A paper plate.

- Hole punch.

- Wool.

- Scissors
  (Ask an adult for help)

- Some colourful ribbon.

- Sticky tape or glue.

- Coloured pens.

- Stickers.

- Other decorations.

HOW TO MAKE YOUR DREAM CATCHER:

1. Cut out the middle of the paper plate leaving a rim of 5 cm all around the edge so that it looks a bit like a bit donut!

2. Decorate what's left of your plate with coloured pens and stickers to bring it to life. Make it really colourful so that you attract the brightest dreams!

IDEAS FOR DECORATIONS:

Craft feathers, Scrunched-up tin foil, Bows—you could use the ones from opened Christmas presents! Small toys from Christmas Crackers, Beads, Bottle caps etc.

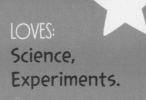

LOVES:
Science,
Experiments.

FAVOURITE MODES
OF TRANSPORT:
Backpack
chopter...
as soon as
she actually
invents it!

FAB FACT:

THE DAHLIA IS
A FLOWER THAT
GROWS IN LOTS
OF DIFFERENT
COLOURS. IT'S
THE NATIONAL
FLOWER
OF MEXICO!

Dahlia is a super smart science guru! She's always doing explosive experiments to create new species of flowers and plants. She keeps pushing herself to create the next amazing invention – and she's come up with some really wacky ideas!

Dahlia gets pretty angry if anyone disturbs her experiments. She also gets frustrated when her test results don't work out as planned. But do you know what? She'll keep trying until she gets that big breakthrough! After all, no one said being a genius would be easy!

DAHLIA'S BRAIN TEASERS...

Super-smart Dahlia has come up with some brain teasers to test the smartest birds in the flock. How well will you do?

FRIENDOKU!

Can you help complete the Sudoku grid, ensuring that every line contains only one of each friend, both up-and-down and left-to-right?

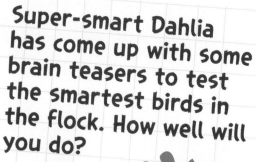

CHEMICAL MIX !

Can you find someone who is not a friend?

Dahlia's chemical formulas hide a secret. Rearrange the chemical symbols to spell out a friend's name.

Ul - Ca

....

W Ow - l (L L)

....

Br An D Sp Ic ES

Se Ta Ll

....

A La D (Hi)

....

Py OP p

....

30

```
C G C B W D A H E A T E D A E
A H F T S E T X A C A Y H B X
N Y E I B F E H S A T T C G P
E F G M A E B C E E J L Z D E
S E C S I K I D A C A A E B R
T L B E A S F E A N F Y G D I
E G P T Y H T A M E B O A C M
I X J H M K A R A I E L D N E
R A P O B D E L Y C A N G A N
O E A F R I E N D S H I P P T
F Q B S E P S R T A D Q U E C
T A V E P L A N T S G E B U A
B W A A L Y A E A V A D C F A
A E R U T A R E P M E T A G B
```

WORD SEARCH

Dahlia doesn't want the most important things in her life to be copied by anyone else - so she's hidden them in this chart! Can you find and circle the following words?

Friendship	Chemistry
Loyalty	Heat
Rebel	Nest
Experiment	Science
Test	Plants
Temperature	Physics

SPOT THE DIFFERENCE

Can you spot the difference in this brainy jumble?

There are 8 differences in all!

PLAY SMART!

NICKNAME: PRANKSTER

Prankster Poppy's wild, mischievous and crazy as a coconut! She lives life in the fast lane and loves acting the fool to make the other birds laugh! Sometimes her practical jokes go a little bit too far, but her friends always forgive her in the end – because that's what friends do!

Poppy can't stand it when people tell her to be quiet. She loves being the centre of attention and she hates being alone.

Her trademark is creating havoc with her drumsticks, banging away on any object to create blazing beats!

LOVES:
Beats and drumming, practical jokes.

FAVOURITE MODES OF TRANSPORT:
Skateboard! Rolling along like a cannonball!

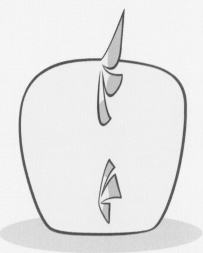

FAB FACT:

WHENEVER POPPY FEELS LONELY SHE LIKES TO WALK ON THE BEACH AND COLLECT WHATEVER HAS WASHED UP ON THE SHORE!

POPPY'S FLOWERING FUNNIES!

WHAT DO YOU GET IF YOU
CROSS A MINION PIG WITH
A FLOWER?

A PORKID!

WHAT TYPE OF MAKE-UP
DOES A FLOWER WEAR?

TUPLIPSTICK!

WHAT DO YOU CALL
A FLOWER'S MOTHER?

CHRYSANTHE-MUM

WHY ARE ROSE STEMS
SO SHARP?

BECAUSE THERE'S
ONE THORN EVERY MINUTE!

WHERE DO FLOWERS WRITE
THEIR HOMEWORK?

IN LILY PADS!

WHAT IS THE STUPIDEST FLOWER
OF ALL?

A DAFTODIL!

WHAT DO YOU CALL
A POSH FLOWER?

A PRIM ROSE!

WHAT HAPPENED TO THE
FLOWER THAT KEPT
SPINNING AROUND?

SHE BECAME DAISY
(DIZZY)!

WHAT IS A FROG'S
FAVOURITE FLOWER?

A CROAK-US!

DID YOU HEAR ABOUT THE
FLOWER GENIUS?

SHE WAS VERY CLOVER (CLEVER)!

BEAT THIS!

WORRIED THAT THE PIGS MIGHT RUMBLE
THE FLOCK'S PLANS, POPPY HAS DESIGNED
A CODE USING HER DRUM BEATS.

TOP SECRET KEY CODE:

A B C D E F G H I

J K L M N O P Q R S T

U V W X Y Z

NICKNAME:

LOVES:
Mud baths,
The Bad Princess.

FAVOURITE MODES OF TRANSPORT:
Walking!
Walking and carrying the Bad Princess!
Walking over to carry the Bad Princess!

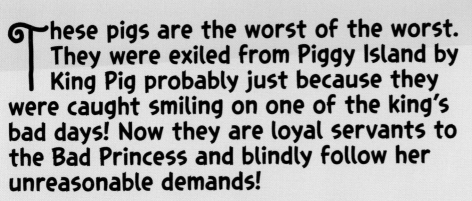

These pigs are the worst of the worst. They were exiled from Piggy Island by King Pig probably just because they were caught smiling on one of the king's bad days! Now they are loyal servants to the Bad Princess and blindly follow her unreasonable demands!

They're dumb, clueless and ultimately harmless. In fact, they'd spend all their time goofing off if they weren't so keen to please the Bad Princess who they believe to be a true royal!

TROTTER CATCH THEM ALL!

THERE ARE SO MANY MINION PIGS ON GOLDEN ISLAND THAT STELLA AND THE FLOCK CAN HARDLY MOVE!

NICKNAME: BABY

ZAP NOW!

This baby bird is the hatchling of the flock, and also the only boy!

Luca is just as playful and cheerful as you'd expect a young bird to be, and he also loves wandering off when no one's looking!

Luca's best trick is his ability to imitate the noises he hears around him. So, although he doesn't speak much himself, he does do great impressions of the rest of the flock.

LOVES:
Attention,
Games.

FAVOURITE MODES
OF TRANSPORT:
Riding piggyback
on one of
the flock!

FAB FACT:

ALTHOUGH HE LOVES BEING FUSSED OVER, LUCA GETS PRETTY MAD WHEN PEOPLE TREAT HIM LIKE A BABY.

LUCA'S LOST!

Oh boy! Luca's wandered off on his own and now he's getting hungry. Can you help him find his way home – and pick up at least five fruits along the way?

Now's your chance to colour Luca. Use the poster to help get his colours right.

THE FRIENDS TEST!

HOW CAN YOU BE SURE YOU'RE DESTINED TO BE BEST FRIENDS FOREVER? SMARTY-PANTS DAHLIA HAS COME UP WITH THIS PERFECT FORMULA FOR FRIENDSHIP.

YOU WILL NEED:

Your first name.
The first name of a friend.
Paper.
Pencil or pen.

REMEMBER:
Dahlia's formula isn't the only guide to friendship! Real friends know that every friendship is an adventure!

HOW TO DO THE FRIENDSHIP TEST:

1. At the top of the page, write down:
YOUR NAME + BFF + YOUR FRIEND'S NAME
For example: STELLA + BFF + POPPY

2. Now count the letters in each name as well as the letters in BFF like so:
STELLA BFF POPPY
   6   3   5

3. Now you need to add each of those numbers to the one that is next to it, which means using the BFF number twice!

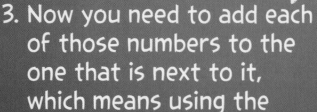

STELLA BFF POPPY

6 + (3) + 5

6 + 3   3 + 5

⭐ 9   8

4. You should end up with two numbers. This is the BFF percentage. So STELLA BFF POPPY = 98% (out of 100)

5. Try it on your friends to see whether your friendship adds up! You could even try it with Stella to see if you could be her best friend forever!

YOUR NAME..

YOUR BFF'S NAME..

IF YOU GET STUCK:

If the number of letters is 10 or more, add those two numbers together before you carry on, like so:

ALEXANDRIA BFF CLAUDIA

10   3   7

1+0

1

Do the same again whenever the numbers add up to two-digit numbers, like so:

ALEXANDRIA BFF CLAUDIA

10   3   7

1 + 0

1

(1 + 3)   (3 + 7)

10

(1 + 0)

4   1

BFF PERCENTAGE = 41%

BFF CERTIFICATE

NOW'S YOUR CHANCE TO MAKE YOUR BFF'S OFFICIAL!

YOU WILL NEED:

1. A scan or photocopy of page 55.
2. Some card (an old cereal or pizza box will do)

3. Paper glue.
4. Scissors (ask an adult to help).
5. A pen or pencil.
6. A Best Friend!

INSTRUCTIONS:

1. Ask an adult to help you cut carefully around the certificate following the dotted lines shown. You can glue it to cardboard as well, if you like.

2. Fill in your name at the top and then add your best friend's name in the space below. You could use coloured pens and even add stickers to make it really special. Remember - your best friend could even be a pet!

3. You also need to sign the certificate to make it official.

4. Present the certificate to your BFF so that they can place it somewhere where everyone will see - maybe even on their bedroom wall!

IF YOU WANT TO FRAME THE CERTIFICATE:

Why not try making a frame out of cardboard? To do this you will need some extra cardboard, perhaps from the back of a cereal box.

1. Cut four strips of cardboard that are the same length as each side of the certificate (two long and two short) and about 2 cm wide.

2. Carefully stick these around the edges of the certificate so that it looks like a frame. Make sure you don't cover any of the certificate!

3. You could decorate the frame with stickers before you present your certificate!

TOP TIP:
WHY NOT ASK YOUR BFF TO HELP MAKE THE CERTIFICATE AND THEN DECORATE IT TOGETHER!

OFFICIAL BFF'S

....

&

....

ARE BEST FRIENDS FOREVER!

MAY THEIR FRIENDSHIP BE FILLED WITH LAUGHTER AND FUN!

FRIEND TREND

Did you know that Stella and Gale – AKA the Bad Princess – used to be best friends? Now's your chance to fix the friendship! But will you patch it up, or wreck it forever?

STELLA START

1 Caught by a strong breeze - roll again.

2 Lost your way - miss a turn.

3 Babysitting Luca - miss a go!

MEND FRIENDSHIP: Whatever you roll must be split between you and the other player. If you roll an odd number, add one to the final score before splitting the move.

2 Given boost by Minion Pigs - roll again.

3 Minion Pig gives wrong directions - miss a go!

4 Friends forever bonus - roll again

1 Crown slips over eyes - miss a turn.

BAD PRINCESS START

5 Minion pigs throw you a party! - miss a go

HOW TO PLAY:

1. First choose who will be Stella and who will be the Bad Princess. The best way to decide is to roll a dice and whoever gets the highest number plays as Stella.

2. Both characters start at their starting points. Don't worry – each track is the same length! Stella goes first.

3. Follow the instructions on the spots.

4. When you reach the "Seeing Red" section, you must decide whether you want to Mend Friendship or End Friendship. If you Mend Friendship you'll help the other player, but that may help yourself too! However, if you End Friendship, you'll try to sabotage the other player.

5. The winner is the player who reaches "Friendship" first!

7 Friends forever bonus – roll again

9 Sing to keep happy – move ahead two squares.

10 Dazzled by sunlight – go back two squares.

10 Minion Pig advice – go forward one spot.

11 Escape sudden storm – go forward two squares.

9 Grab for Golden Egg – move back two squares.

END FRIENDSHIP: Whatever you throw is used only by the other player, who must move backwards that number of spaces.

14 Lost your way – miss a turn.

15 Friends forever bonus – roll again

16 Tempers flareed! – go back to start!

15 Friends forever bonus – roll again

16 Blinded by pride, power, and greed – go back to start!

FRIENDSHIP!

ARE YOU BAD ENOUGH?

COULD YOU BE A BAD PRINCESS? TRY THIS QUIZ TO FIND OUT! JUST REMEMBER THAT THE RIGHT ANSWERS ARE THE ONES THAT SEEM MOST WRONG!

1. What's your favourite headgear?

a. Flowers in my hair.
b. A floppy hat.
c. A crown.

2. Where would you like to live?

a. In a cool nest with all my friends.
b. On the beach so that I could sleep under the stars.
c. In a cold castle far from everyone else who's jealous of me.

3. Friends are:

a. The people you can rely on.
b. The people you'd do anything for.
c. An inconvenience.

4. My favourite jewellery would be:

a. A sparkly bracelet.
b. A homemade necklace with a shell hanging from it.
c. A royal sceptre.

5. My favourite way to get around quickly is:

a. On my bike.
b. On roller-skates.
c. On the shoulders of my minions.

6. Your best friend is ill. Do you...?

a. Make her a thoughtful "Get Well Soon" card.
b. Visit her every day.
c. Wonder if it's catching!

7. What is your favourite kind of fruit?

a. Something that fits in my lunchbox, like a banana or an apple.
b. Something that tastes good with cream, like strawberries or raspberries.
c. Grapes that have been peeled by my minions.

8. You're having a party. Would the invitations say...?

a. Come and play!
b. Everyone's welcome- bring a friend!
c. By royal appointment only.

9. What's your favourite boat?

a. A sail boat.
b. A raft made of driftwood.
c. A royal barge.

10. You've just moved, but your new bedroom is a bit gloomy. Do you...?

a. Make some fun plans to redecorate as soon as you can.
b. Jazz up the walls with some posters.
b. Knock down the room with a bulldozer and start again!

11. Where do you most like to play?

a. The park.
b. The beach.
c. In your private courtyard surrounded by guards and a moat.

12. If you could change one thing in the world what would it be?

a. Make the summers longer. More time to play!
b. Protect the environment by recycling as much as I can.
c. Rule it with an iron fist!

13. You discover you secretly have a twin sister. Would you...?

a. Try on each other's clothes.
b. Introduce her to all your friends.
c. Lock her up! There's only room for one princess in your world!

14. The sweets you've bought are your best friend's favourite. Do you...?

a. Divide the sweets up evenly.
b. Give your best friend all the sweets – she'd do the same for you!
c. Find a new friend.

15. It's raining and you wanted to go out to play. Do you...?

a. Find something to do indoors until the shower passes.
b. Splash in the puddles – at least the rain can water the plants!
c. Command the rain to stop, by royal decree.

ANSWERS:

MOSTLY As.

You're a good friend, loyal and always thinking of others. You're most like Stella.

MOSTLY Bs.

You're a dreamer who thinks a lot about others. You're most like Willow.

MOSTLY Cs.

You know what you want and you're not afraid to tread on a few toes to get it. Just like Bad Princess!

TIME TO PLAY!

These feathery friends are heading out to play.
Can you find this fun five in the sequence?

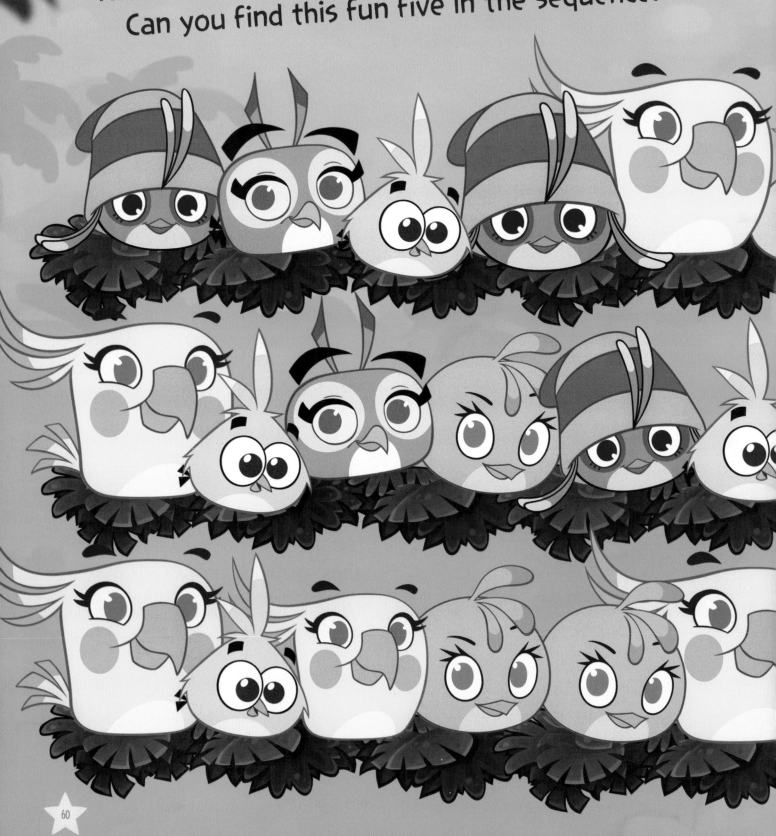

Keep your eyes peeled for this sequence!

ZAP NOW!

HIDE AND SNEAK!

One day, Luca thought he had found the perfect hiding place for hide and seek...

Where is Luca?

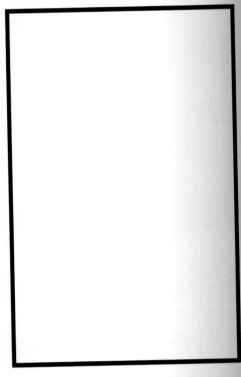

CAN YOU HELP WITH THIS STORY? WE'VE GIVEN YOU THE START AND THE END – BUT YOU'LL NEED TO MAKE UP THE REST AND DRAW IT IN THE PANELS.

Luca is with the rest of the flock once more, who are all pleased.

Next time we play hide and seek –

– maybe I'd better be the one who hides!

THE SNEAKY END...

FIERCE FRIENDS!

Add a splash of colour to the flock!

START HERE!

HOME!

A MILLION MINIONS!

THOSE DOPEY MINION PIGS ARE BLOCKING STELLA'S WAY HOME! HELP STELLA NAVIGATE THE MAZE WITHOUT BUMPING INTO ANY PIGS...

CAN YOU FIND...

I x pig eating an ice cream..........................

3 x pigs with gum on their faces..............

I x pig with his back to the maze.............

2 x romantic pigs......................

3 x angry pigs.........................

I x upside down pig...................

TIP: YOU HAD BETTER STAY AWAY FROM THE BAD PRINCESS. SHE LEADS STRAIGHT TO A DEAD END!

MAKE-IT HAPPEN!

SILLY BIRDS!

WHAT YOU NEED:
Yellow paper, White paper,
Scissors (ask an adult for help),
Black pencil or pen,
Sticky tape.

HOW TO MAKE IT:
Take a sheet of yellow paper and fold it across the diagonal to make a triangle. This is the beak of your bird, which can open and close! Next, use a template to make two circles out of the white paper.

To do this, draw around something circular like a coin or a jar (think about how big you need it to be!). These will be the bird's eyes. Finally, draw two black spots in the centre of the eyes with your pencil or pen. Now you just need to find somewhere to put it all together – maybe on your bedroom door! Check with your Mum or Dad before sticking it up with sticky tape – they can even help you to get it looking right!

THE RESULT:
A cute bird face! You can make these for any occasion by using different sizes of paper – you could even stick the face to the front of a birthday card for a friend!

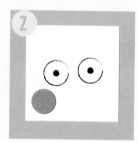

HAPPY BIRTHDAY!

ASK A GROWN-UP TO HELP WITH SCISSORS.

PRETTY DAISY BOOKMARK

WHAT YOU NEED:
Thin green cardboard, Scissors (ask an adult for help),
Paints – yellow and white.

HOW TO MAKE IT:
Cut out a length of cardboard for the bookmark. It should be taller than a book (about 18 cm is fine) and about 3 cm across. Use the scissors to cut lines in one end to make a fringe. Using the paint, add in the daisies. This is so easy that you don't even need a brush!

* First dip your thumb into the yellow paint and then press it onto the card to make the centre of the daisies.
* Do the same again with the white paint, but this time use your finger – this will be smaller and it will become the petals. You need to press the white paint in a circle around the yellow centres, roughly 6-8 times in total to make the petals.

THE RESULT:
A personalised bookmark. Now all you need is to decide what book to read!

CUTE BUTTON NECKLACE

WHAT YOU NEED:
Some pretty coloured buttons, Some coloured string, Scissors,
(ask an adult for help)

HOW TO MAKE IT:
This make-it needs a grown up's help, but is worth it to create some special jewellery just for you. First, ask the grown-up to cut a length of string that wraps easily around your neck.

The length needs to be long enough that it can dangle freely, and still have enough at the back to tie together easily.

TIP: THE IDEAL LENGTH CAN WRAP AROUND YOUR NECK TWICE.

Next, choose a colourful button and thread it along the string.
If the button has four holes, you should only use the top two.
If it only has two holes, thread the string through both.
Once you're finished, tie the string around your neck.

You can choose to add as many or as few buttons as you like. Try experimenting with three, five and just one to see what looks best.

THE RESULT:
A special necklace that you can show off to your friends!

TOP TIP: WHY NOT MAKE A NECKLACE FOR YOUR BEST FRIEND, TOO?

MY TREE PAINTING

WHAT YOU NEED:
Paper, Coloured pencil or pen, Pink paint.

HOW TO MAKE IT:
First, use the pencil or pen to draw a tree trunk with branches. It should be about two-thirds as tall as the paper. If you're not sure how to draw this, try copying a twig from the park or your garden – you could even stick a stick to the page instead! Now comes the messy part. Dip your fingers into the pink paint until they are nice and gooey. Then press each finger onto the paper so that they look like the blossoms of the tree. You need lots of colourful blossoms to really bring it to life. Once you've added enough blossoms, leave the picture to dry.

THE RESULT:
It's a tree made from your own fingerprints! Fingerprints are unique which means nobody else can ever make one quite like it!

INVENT-A-STORY

One day Stella was...

on the beach.

in the tree house.

eating breakfast.

Stella investigated and found...

Luca trapped in a net.

Minion Pigs singing an awful song.

Stella soon discovered that...

she was trapped.

she was surrounded.

Just then the Bad Princess arrived...

and laughed wickedly at Stella's predicament.

and sneered at the thought of helping Stella.

The Bad Princess was laughing so much that she...

slipped and fell!

tumbled into the trap herself!

The Bad Princess...

bumped into Stella

pushed Stella aside

freeing Stella quite by accident! Now it was the Bad Princess that was trapped...

Stella helped the Bad Princess

Stella told the Minion Pigs where their mistress was trapped

and soon the Bad Princess was free.

WHO IS THE MOST FAMOUS PIG SCIENTIST?

ALBERT SWINESTEIN!

WHO IS THE SECOND MOST FAMOUS PIG SCIENTIST?

STEPHEN PORKING!

a rock slide had crashed down and blocked the path.

she couldn't go any further.

WHICH FAMOUS SCIENTIST WAS THE HEAVIEST?

ISAAC TWO-TON!

slid down a steep slope and dented her crown!

knocked over the obstacle

WHICH FAMOUS INVENTOR LOVED TO SING?

THOMAS EDISONG!

Stella asked the rest of the flock to come and help

Although they weren't friends anymore, the Bad Princess had to say "Thank you" to Stella. But maybe one day they would be friends again.

The end.

POPPY'S PRANKS!

Here are some of poppy's favourite practical jokes for you to try on your friends and family.

WORMY APPLE!

YOU WILL NEED:

An apple from the fruit bowl, A gummy worm, A pencil.

Take an apple from the fruit bowl and use a pencil to poke a hole in its skin. Once there's a big enough hole, push the end of a gummy worm into the hole so that the rest pokes out. Then replace it in the fruit bowl. Wait for someone to eat the apple. You can just imagine their surprise when they bite in and find a worm!

LITTLE FEET!

YOU WILL NEED:

Tissues (toilet paper or kitchen roll is fine). Shoes belonging to a family member or friend.

While no one's looking, take some clean tissues and push them into the toes of someone else's shoes. It could be a family member or your best friend! Get quite a few in there but make sure it's not obvious from the outside. The next time they put their shoes on they'll find they're a lot tighter than before – they can hardly get their feet in them. Try to keep a straight face as you tell them that their feet must have grown!

HEAD OVER HEELS!

YOU WILL NEED:

To be in the living room on your own.

Perhaps your family has pictures of you, your brother, your sister or gran on the mantelpiece or by the television. If so, try turning them upside down while no one's looking. The trick is to make sure they are in exactly the same place as before, only upside down – so take care to note exactly where they started. Once the pictures are upside down you just need to see how long it takes for anyone to notice. If it takes a long time, you could try standing on your head and saying that "everything seems normal this way up!"

1. Remember to always choose someone who can take a joke.

2. Choose the right time for your pranks so that everyone can appreciate them. It's no good setting up practical jokes when people are hurrying to go on holiday or going to an interview, for instance. Try a Saturday or Sunday afternoon!

3. Practical jokes take cunning – you have to set them up while no one else is looking, so plan in advance and come prepared.

4. Always own up to your practical jokes after they've struck. That includes telling the victim!

5. It's a good idea to give a reward to the victim to show that they've been a good sport – maybe a sweet or just saying thank you!

6. Remember that the practical joker can become the victim, too. So if you perform a successful practical joke – watch out, someone may be looking to get you back!

HERE COMES THE BRIDE!

YOU WILL NEED:

A plastic cup. Some coloured bits of paper. Scissors.

Take a plastic cup and fill it with confetti. You can make your own confetti by cutting up coloured paper into little squares - keep them small, just a couple of centimetres across is fine. Next, go to a room while no one's looking - a bedroom is funniest.

The room must have a door which you can leave slightly open. Using a chair, climb up so that you can reach the top of the door. Pull the door as closed as you can so you are still able to reach your hand through the gap - it doesn't need to be really closed, just so long as it's not wide enough for a person to walk through. Now, place your cup of confetti by balancing it on the top of the door - propping it against the frame so that it is coming towards you works best.

Then, put the chair back where you found it and hide the evidence! The next person who opens the door will be showered in confetti! If you wait for them to appear, you could sing "Here comes the bride" to them!

BITTER TOOTHPASTE

YOU WILL NEED:

A family member's toothbrush. Salt.

Sprinkle a little salt on a family member's toothbrush before they clean their teeth - you could do this during the day, it doesn't have to be right before. When they clean their teeth, the toothpaste will taste bitter instead of fresh! Don't worry - salt's good for the gums and won't hurt them.

Ask an adult for help!

73

STELLA QUIZ

SO YOU THINK YOU KNOW ALL ABOUT STELLA!
SEE IF YOU CAN ANSWER THESE TRICKY QUESTIONS...

1. Which bird has bright pink feathers?

....

2. Which mean-spirited bird leads the Minion Pigs?

....

3. Which dreamer bird wears a floppy hat?

....

4. Who is the baby of the flock?

....

5. Which bird is this?

SMARTY!

6. What is the name of the island where Stella and the flock live?

....

7. Who is the prankster of the flock?

....

8. What does the Bad Princess wear to ensure that the pigs obey her?

....

9. What precious item is the Bad Princess searching for?

....

10. Which member of the flock loves science and inventing?

....

74

ANSWERS...

PAGE 11: Spot The Difference

PAGE 30: Friendoku

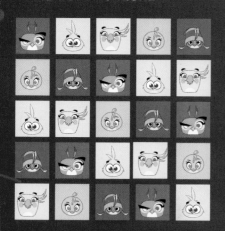

PAGE 30: Chemical Mix

Luca, Willow, Bad Princess, Stella, Dahlia, Poppy

PAGE 31: Wordsearch

PAGE 32: Spot The Difference

PAGE 39: Beat This

Hey guys,
Let's have a party tonight down by the beach. The party starts at midnight with singing karaoke and plenty of yummy food! Bring your best dance moves and prepare to rock out!
See you there!
Poppy x x x

PAGE 40-41: Trotter Catch them all!

PAGE 48-49: Luca's Lost!

PAGE 60-61: Time to Play!

PAGE 66-67: Millions of Minions

PAGE 74-75: Stella Quiz

1. Stella
2. Bad princess
3. Willow
4. Luca
5. Dahlia
6. Golden Island
7. Poppy
8. A crown
9. The Golden Egg
10. Dahlia
11. Gale
12. Poppy
13. Luca
14. Poppy
15. A castle